big
NATE

big NATE

MAKES THE GRADE

by LINCOLN PEIRCE

SCHOLASTIC INC.

ISBN 978-0-545-52884-9

Big Nate Makes the Grade copyright © 2012 by United Feature Syndicate, Inc.
All rights reserved. Published by Scholastic Inc., 557 Broadway, New York, NY 10012,
by arrangement with Andrews McMeel Publishing, LLC, an Andrews McMeel Universal company.
SCHOLASTIC and associated logos are trademarks and/or registered trademarks of Scholastic Inc.

12 11 10 9 8 7 6 5 4 3   12 13 14 15 16 17/0

Printed in the U.S.A.   23

First Scholastic printing, November 2012

SHOPPING FOR BACK-TO-SCHOOL CLOTHES IS USUALLY A TOTAL WASTE OF TIME, BUT **THIS** YEAR I'M ON A **MISSION**!

I'VE **GOT** TO FIND MY-SELF A NEW PAIR OF LUCKY SOCKS! MY OLD ONES HAVE JUST ABOUT **HAD** IT!

THEY'VE RUN OUT OF LUCK, EH?

NO, THEY HAVEN'T RUN OUT OF LUCK, FOOL! DO THESE LOOK LIKE THEY'VE RUN OUT OF LUCK?

FROM A SOCK'S PERSPEC-TIVE, YES.

NOT WASHING 'EM! **THAT'S** WHAT KEEPS 'EM LUCKY!

IT'S GONNA BE TOUGH TO FIND NEW SOCKS AS LUCKY AS THESE.

exCUSE ME, BUT ON WHAT BASIS DO YOU CALL THOSE SOCKS **LUCKY?**

WHILE WEARING THOSE SOCKS, YOU'VE BEEN PUT ON ACADEMIC PROBATION, RECEIVED 237 DETENTIONS, BEEN REJECTED REPEATEDLY BY JENNY, AND LED THE SOCCER TEAM TO AN 0-AND-14 SEASON!

EXACTLY! THINK WHAT COULD'VE HAPPENED IF I **HADN'T** BEEN WEARING THESE!

I OBVIOUSLY KNOW NOTHING ABOUT LUCKY SOCKS.

THAT'S WHAT I WAS ABOUT TO SAY, BUT I FIGURED I'D SPARE YOUR FEELINGS.

♪

HEY, EMMITT!

WELL! WHAT ARE YOU GENTS DOING HERE? SCHOOL DOESN'T START 'TIL TUESDAY!

WE KNOW!

BUT THERE'S SOMETHING I NEED TO CHECK OUT IN MRS. GODFREY'S ROOM!

BE RIGHT BACK!

IT'S **STILL THERE!**

IT **IS?**

WA HA HA
HA HA HA HA
HA HA HA
HA
HA

I CAN'T BELIEVE IT'S STILL THERE!

HA HA HA HA

TOLD YA!

HA HA HA HA

A CUSTODIAN KNOWS EVERYTHING, AND A CUSTODIAN KNOWS NOTHING.

13

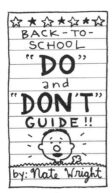

☆★☆★☆★☆
BACK-TO-
SCHOOL
"DO"
and
"DON'T"
GUIDE!!
by: Nate Wright

DO: Ride the bus!!

PAR-TAY!

Dang! Turn off the 'N Sync!

SCHOOL DISTRICT 3

DON'T: Get driven to school by a parent!

Remember to use those "handi-wipes" after lunch!

I love you, son!

DO: Get back-to-school supplies!

This notebook holds 6 candy bars AND a juice box!

Cool!

DON'T: Get a back-to-school haircut!

What's with the hat?

None o' your beeswax.

DO: Talk to "new kids"!

Well hel-LO there!

Can I show you around?

DON'T: Talk to new teachers!

...And what's your APPROACH to teach-ing math?

What a BROWN-NOSE!

Let's wedgie him later!

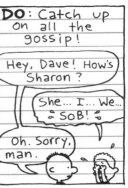

DO: Catch up on all the gossip!

Hey, Dave! How's Sharon?

She... I... We... SOB!

Oh. Sorry, man.

DON'T: Ask Kevin Gladchuk "how was your summer?"

Funny you should ask. I have here some photos...

DO: Stand up to 7th-grade bullies!

DON'T! DON'T!!

HEY, GUYS! JOIN IN!

TRASH

MR. ROSA, I'M READY TO HAVE A **GREAT** YEAR IN ART CLASS! YOU ARE LOOKING AT AN **ART TSUNAMI!**

MY CREATIVE JUICES ARE BUBBLING LIKE **MOLTEN LAVA!** I'M AN ARTISTIC BREAKTHROUGH WAITING TO HAPPEN!

READY THE DISPLAY CASE IN CORRIDOR THREE! I'LL HAVE IT FILLED WITH MASTERPIECES BEFORE YOU CAN SAY "PICASSO"!

SUDDENLY I'M THINKING TOMORROW'S "SOCK PUPPET" ASSIGNMENT MIGHT BE A HARD SELL.

I'LL BET MRS. GODFREY READS ME THE RIOT ACT ABOUT NOT GETTING INTO TROUBLE THIS YEAR.

SO TALK TO HER **FIRST!**

TELL HER YOU'RE GOING TO BE A MODEL STUDENT THIS YEAR! FIRE A PRE-EMPTIVE STRIKE!

A PRE-EMPTIVE STRIKE?

A PRE-EMPTIVE STRIKE!

MRS. GODFREY, I JUST WANT YOU TO KNOW THAT THIS YEAR I'M GO—...

NATE, I'M BUSY RIGHT NOW. SIT DOWN, PLEASE.

BUT CAN I JUST TELL YOU THAT I'M....

NATE, DID YOU HEAR WHAT I SAID? SIT **DOWN**, PLEASE!

LOOK, ALL I'M TRYING TO SAY IS...

NATE! I'VE TOLD YOU **TWICE** ALREADY!

NOW, FOR THE **THIRD** TIME... **SIT DOWN!!**

THREE PRE-EMPTIVE STRIKES AND YOU'RE OUT.

WHAT'S UP WITH YOU AND **GINA**, NATE?

YEAH! ALL YOU TWO DO IS **ARGUE** ALL THE TIME!

HEY, YOU WOULD **TOO** IF SHE SAT NEXT TO **YOU!** SHE THINKS SHE'S SO GREAT, BUT **MAN!**... SHE IS JUST TOTALLY **OBNOXIOUS!**

NATE AND GINA HAVE A "LOVE-HATE" THING GOING ON!

EX**ACT**LY! SHE'S COM-PLETELY...

!... **NO!!** NOT "LOVE-HATE"!! JUST **HATE!** IT'S ALL **HATE!**

OOOOOOH!

I WONDER WHY MRS. GODFREY HATES ME SO MUCH.

THERE'S GOT TO BE **SOME** REASON, BUT FOR THE LIFE OF ME I CAN'T FIGURE OUT WHAT IT IS.

HEY! WHY DON'T WE THINK OF ALL THE THINGS **WE** HATE ABOUT YOU, AND CROSS-REFERENCE THEM WITH STUFF **SHE** MIGHT DESPISE!

GOOD IDEA!

WELL, THERE'S HIS VOICE!

IT'S SO **NASAL!**

sigh...

YESSSS! I GOT A HUNDRED AND FIVE ON THE TEST!

A HUNDRED AND **FIVE**??

GINA, YOU CAN'T GET HIGHER THAN A HUNDRED!

WELL, **I** DID! HERE'S WHAT HAPPENED:

DURING THE TEST, I NOTICED THAT MRS. GODFREY HAD MADE A TYPOGRAPHICAL ERROR ON QUESTION SIX!

I CORRECTED HER MISTAKE, AND SHE GAVE ME FIVE POINTS EXTRA CREDIT!

HMMM

SO IF **I** NOTICE A MISTAKE THAT MRS. GODFREY MADE, MAYBE **I'LL** GET EXTRA CREDIT!

MAYBE! WORKED FOR ME!

MRS. GODFREY?

MMM?

BOY, DID YOU EVER SCREW UP ON QUESTION EIGHT! LET ME SHOW YOU...

FOR YOU, SHE GIVETH. FOR ME, SHE TAKETH AWAY.

Peirce

33

SIMPLE AND TO THE POINT: "NATE FOR TREASURER"!

EXCEPT YOU DON'T EVEN **WANT** TO BE TREASURER! YOU JUST WANT TO BEAT **GINA**!

LOOK, FRANCIS, GINA'S GOOD AT **EVERY**THING! SHE'S NEVER COME IN **SECOND** HER WHOLE LIFE! THAT'S NOT **HEALTHY**!

AFTER ELECTION DAY, SHE'LL HAVE TO COPE WITH **FAILURE** FOR A CHANGE! BY BEATING HER, I'LL BE TEACHING HER A VALUABLE LIFE LESSON!

THAT'S JUST THE SORT OF WARPED LOGIC YOU LOOK FOR IN A CLASS TREASURER.

PLUS, IT'LL BE **FUN**!

SO, WHAT DID MY "WORTHY OPPONENT" SAY WHEN YOU INTERVIEWED **HER** FOR THE PAPER?

HOW COME YOU KEEP DOING THAT?

DOING WHAT?

THAT THING WITH YOUR FINGERS. YOU DO IT WHENEVER YOU SAY "WORTHY OPPONENT."

SO?

SO, IT JUST DOESN'T SEEM ALL THAT... RESPECTFUL.

OOOOH, **CRISIS**! I'M NOT BEING "RE**SPECT**FUL"!

SOME ARTICLES WRITE THEMSELVES.

38

HEY! I'M NATE WRIGHT, CANDIDATE FOR TREASURER! WHO ARE YOU GONNA VOTE FOR?

I'M UNDECIDED.

OH, COME **ON**! YOU CAN'T SERIOUSLY BE THINKING ABOUT VOTING FOR **GINA**! I MEAN, GIVE ME A **BREAK**!

SHE'S SO **ANNOYING**! SHE'S SO **STUCK-UP**! IS **THAT** WHAT YOU WANT? **THINK**! THE CHOICE BETWEEN HER AND ME IS A **NO-BRAINER**!

OK, I'M NOT UNDECIDED ANYMORE.

THERE, WAS THAT SO HARD?

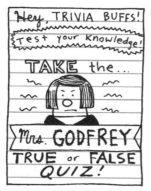

Hey, TRIVIA BUFFS! Test your knowledge! TAKE the... Mrs. GODFREY TRUE or FALSE QUIZ!

TRUE or FALSE: In her high school yearbook, Mrs. Godfrey listed her "hobbies" as "unprovoked rage" and "lunch."

What are YOU lookin' at? HUH?

TRUE or FALSE: At their wedding, Mrs. Godfrey insisted her husband promise to "love, honor, and cower in fear."

Whatever you say, dear!

TRUE or FALSE: In "The Two Towers", Mrs. Godfrey makes a cameo appearance as "Orc #3."

AAARRGHHH

Gandalf! HELP!

TRUE or FALSE: Mrs. Godfrey's breath has been classified as a "weapon of mass destruction."

tuna meat loaf cheese cabbage mold rotten eggs

TRUE or FALSE: To pay for college, Mrs. Godfrey worked part-time as a Slim-Fast "before" model.

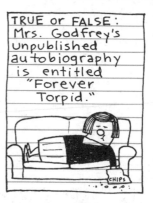

TRUE or FALSE: Mrs. Godfrey's unpublished autobiography is entitled "Forever Torpid."

CHIPS

CHECK IT OUT! TRUE OR FALSE?

! !

TRUE. SO TRUE. AGAIN?

DETENTION

Peirce

...AND FINALLY, TODAY'S FIELD HOCKEY GAME AGAINST BAILEY HAS BEEN POSTPONED UNTIL FRIDAY.

THAT CONCLUDES THIS MORNING'S ANNOUNCEMENTS. PRETTY DULL, EH, GANG? MORNING ANNOUNCEMENTS ARE ONE BIG **SNOOZE-FEST** INSTEAD OF BEING WHAT THEY **COULD** BE: AN **EVENT!**

...AND SO, STARTING TODAY, YOURS TRULY WILL ENDEAVOR TO MAKE OUR TIME TO-GETHER EACH MORNING JUST A BIT MORE MEMORABLE!

PLYMOUTH

GUY WALKS INTO A BAR WITH A DUCK ON HIS HEAD...

NATE...

Peirce

NATE, I'M AFRAID I CAN'T ALLOW YOU TO TELL JOKES OVER THE INTERCOM DURING MORNING ANNOUNCEMENTS.

BUT WHY NOT?

BECAUSE IT HAS NOTHING TO DO WITH **SCHOOL**, THAT'S WHY!

AH! GOTCHA!

SO IF I TOLD A JOKE THAT **DID** HAVE SOMETHING TO DO WITH SCHOOL, THAT WOULD BE OK!

HEY, GANG! HOW MANY MATH TEACHERS DOES IT TAKE TO SCREW IN A LIGHTBULB?

STOP.

Peirce

FINALLY, TODAY'S LUNCH WILL BE FISH STICKS, TATER TOTS, FRUIT CUP AND RAISIN COOKIES.

AND NOW FOR A BRIEF EDITORIAL.

WHEN AN INDIVIDUAL WANTS TO INJECT A TINY BIT OF LEVITY INTO THE SCHOOL DAY AND IS **DENIED** THE CHANCE TO DO SO... **THAT**, MY FRIENDS, IS **CENSORSHIP!**

AND CENSORSHIP IS **WRONG!** DOESN'T SCHOOL TEACH US ABOUT FREE SPEECH? SHOULDN'T MORNING ANNOUNCEMENTS BE A TIME FOR OUR VOICES TO BE **HEARD?** I SAY **YES!!**

THAT CONCLUDES THIS BRIEF EDITORIAL.

...AND NOW, **DESPITE** THE FACT THAT THE SCHOOL IS TRYING TO **MUZZLE** ME, I WILL TELL THIS MORNING'S "JOKE OF THE DAY!"

KNOCK KNOCK

AH! HEAR THAT, FOLKS? MR. NICHOLS IS FINALLY GETTING INTO THE SPIRIT OF THINGS WITH A **KNOCK KNOCK** JOKE! WHO'S THERE, MR. NICHOLS?

ANGRY PRINCIPAL.

ANGRY PRINCIPAL **WHO?**

ANGRY PRINCIPAL WHO'S ABOUT TO SEND YOU TO DETENTION.

I DON'T GET IT.

WHATCHA GOT?

AN OLD YEARBOOK!

OVER IN THE REFERENCE STACKS THEY HAVE COPIES OF EVERY YEARBOOK IN THE SCHOOL'S **HISTORY!**

COOL!

THIS ONE'S FROM TWENTY YEARS AGO! IT'S TOTALLY **HILARIOUS!**

QUIET PLEASE

IS THAT... MR. **GALVIN**?

HEE HEE! YUP! HE WAS ACTUALLY **YOUNG** ONCE!

WOW! LOOK AT MRS. BELLAMY!

SNICKER! TWENTY YEARS AND **FORTY POUNDS** AGO!

QU PLE

HEY! IS MR. ROSA IN THERE?

LET'S SEE...

FLIP FLIP

MMPH! NICE **HAIR!**

SNORT! NICE **DISCO** SHIRT!

HA HA HA

HA HEE HEE

HA HA

HELLO, BOYS.

WA HA HA A HA HA HA HA HA HA HA

THIS IS WHY, DURING FREE PERIODS, I TEND TO STAY IN MY CLASSROOM WITH THE DOOR LOCKED.

HA HA HA HA

HE'S A DISCO INFERNO!

HA HA

HA HA

"FROM BENEATH HER ROCK SHE OOZES, HER DISGUSTING BREATH REEKING OF SPAM."

HEE HEE! I WROTE ANOTHER HILARIOUS HAIKU ABOUT MRS. GODFREY!

LISTEN TO THIS! IT'S SEVENTEEN SYLLABLES OF SHEER POETRY!

✳AHEM!✳ "SHE IS A MONSTER: A BLOATED OBSCENITY."...

AND SHE'S RIGHT BEHIND YOU.

NO, THAT'S **EIGHTEEN** SYLLABLES! CAN'T YOU **COUNT?**

SO! YOU WROTE SOME SORT OF **POEM** ABOUT ME?

WHAT? I...I... N-**NO!**

IT DOESN'T EVEN MENTION YOUR **NAME**, SEE? WHAT MAKES YOU THINK IT'S ABOUT **YOU**?

I COULD BE REFERRING TO SOME **OTHER** "BLOATED OBSCENITY"!

SIGH...

DETENTION

YOU AGAIN?

I'M SORRY TO HEAR ABOUT YOUR FAMILY EMERGENCY, NATE. WOULD YOU LIKE TO TALK ABOUT IT?

UH... NO, IT... UM... IT'S TOO PAIN- FUL.

MRS. GODFREY

WELL, DON'T KEEP IT ALL BOTTLED UP! THAT WILL JUST MAKE IT HARDER TO HANDLE!

IF YOU DON'T WANT TO TALK TO A TEACH- ER OR COUNSELOR, AT LEAST FIND A **FRIEND** YOU CAN CONFIDE IN!

OKAY...

PSST! I'VE GOT MRS. GODFREY EATING OUT OF MY HAND!

THIS "FAMILY EMERGENCY" EXCUSE IS THE BEST IDEA I'VE EVER HAD! IT WORKS LIKE A **CHARM!**

NOT ONLY DOES IT GET ME OUT OF DOING HOMEWORK, BUT THE PHRASE "FAMILY EMERGENCY" SOUNDS TOO **PERSONAL** FOR MRS. GODFREY TO ASK FOR ANY DETAILS!

BUT THERE **AREN'T** ANY DETAILS, BECAUSE THE WHOLE THING IS **BOGUS!** RIGHT?

EXACTLY! IT'S **GENIUS!**

HOW 'BOUT A HIGH FIVE?

I'M LEANING MORE TOWARD A SIMPLE SLAP IN THE FACE.

SO MRS. GODFREY FOUND OUT YOUR "FAMILY EMERGENCY" WAS A SHAM, HUH?

DID SHE EVER.

NOT ONLY DID SHE TIP OFF MY DAD, SHE'S MAKING ME DO ALL THE HOMEWORK I MISSED, **PLUS** AN EXTRA BOOK REPORT, **PLUS** DETENTION UNTIL THANKSGIVING!!

NOT TO MENTION THE FACT THAT, HAVING DONE SOMETHING SO DECEITFUL, YOU'VE PROBABLY LOST A LOT OF SELF-RESPECT.

HUH?

FORGET IT.

OH, HOW I HATE HER.

OKAY, KID, BIG SMILE!

HOLD IT! WHAT ABOUT MY BLACK EYE?

WHAT ABOUT IT?

WELL, CAN'T YOU COVER IT UP? USE SOME SORT OF SPECIAL LIGHT OR LENS OR SOMETHING?

"I'M A **DOCTOR**, JIM, NOT A **MAGICIAN!**"

STAR TREK: EPISODE 47, SCENE 32!

HA HA HA

HA HA HA

NOTICE HOW I ESTABLISH RAPPORT BY REFERENCING POP CULTURE.

WHAT A TWIT.

HERE, KID... I'LL PUT A LITTLE CONCEALER OVER THAT SHINER.

SMILE!

THIS STUFF IS TICKLY.

NOW WE'LL LET THE MAGIC OF PHOTOGRAPHY DO THE REST!

I... I THINK... I'M GONNA... AH... AHH...

BIG SMILE, KID! SHOW ME SOME TEETH!

CHOO!

MAGIC!

KLIK!

Peirce

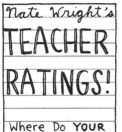

Nate Wright's

TEACHER RATINGS!

Where Do **YOUR** Teachers Rate in the **HALL** OF **SHAME**?

MR. STAPLES (Math)

" < fun "

Today, the fascinating world of... FRACTIONS!

RATING: 2.0

MRS. BRINDLE (LIFE SKILLS)

"A recipe for disaster"

...and after 20 minutes, our "johnny-cake" is done!

RATING: 1.3

MS. LA CHANCE (French)

"Ooh La Loser"

Let the words RRRRROLL off your tongue!

RATING: 0.8

MR. GALVIN (Science)

"Boredom = mc^2"

You don't know what I'm saying, do you? Well, I don't know what I'm saying either.

RATING: 1.4

MR. ALDRIDGE (Computer Lab)

Press "escape"

Wait. Wait. That wasn't supposed to... okay, wait. Wait.

tik tak tik tak tik tak

RATING: 1.1

MRS. GODFREY (Social Studies)

"Oh, the humanity."

I summon thee, hounds of Satan!

RATING: −3,000,000

DO YOU ACTUALLY EXPECT ME TO PUT THIS IN THE DISPLAY CASE?

THINK OF IT AS A PUBLIC SERVICE!

G is for the Gruesome class she teaches;

O is for Obese, it's plain to see.

D is for her favorite Dinner: leeches.

F, the grade she gives most Frequently.

R is for her Rages never-ending;

E, her Evil Eye which never blinks.

Y is for my Youth which I am spending

sitting in detention.

MAN, THIS STINKS.

I GOT A **HUNDRED** ON THE MATH TEST! WHAT DID **YOU** GET?

WHAT DOES IT MATTER?

I DON'T MEASURE MY WORTH BASED ON MY **GRADE POINT AVERAGE!** I'M NOT DEFINED BY MY SCORE ON SOME **MATH TEST!**

HEY, LOOK! THERE'S THAT KID WHO GOT A **36** ON THE MATH TEST!

YOU WERE SAYING?

HEY! **HEY!** IT WAS A **38**!

HI, MRS. SHIPULSKI.

HELLO, NATE.

I'M HERE TO SEE PRINCIPAL NICHOLS.

YOU'LL HAVE TO WAIT. ARTUR IS IN WITH HIM RIGHT NOW.

!! ARTUR !!

MM-HM. HAVE A SEAT.

WELL, **WELL!** WHO WOULD'VE **THUNK** IT!

ARTUR IS IN THE **PRINCIPAL'S** OFFICE! I GUESS **MR. PERFECT** MUST HAVE **SCREWED UP!**

PRETTY **QUIET** IN THERE!

※CHUCKLE!※ ARTUR MUST BE SQUIRMING IN HIS SEAT WHILE NICHOLS GIVES HIM THE **HAIRY EYEBALL!**

WONDERFUL JOB, ARTUR! IT'S BEEN **THIRTY YEARS** SINCE ONE OF OUR STUDENTS EARNED THE CITYWIDE "GOOD CITIZENSHIP" AWARD!

YOU'VE MADE US VERY PROUD, SON!

WE'LL PUT YOUR PLAQUE IN THE DISPLAY CASE IMMEDIATELY!

THANK YOU, SIR.

OH, HOW I HATE HIM.

NEXT?

IN THE FIRST ROUND, YOU'RE PLAYING SOME-BODY FROM BAILEY MIDDLE SCHOOL... DEREK NACK.

DEREK NACK?

TOURNAMENT

DEREK NACK... HMMM... THAT NAME SOUNDS FAMILIAR... THAT NAME SOUNDS **VERY** FAMILIAR.

I MUST HAVE PLAYED HIM BEFORE, BUT I CAN'T REMEMBER IT. MAYBE WHEN I SEE HIM, IT'LL ALL COME BACK TO...

NATE!!

YIP!

PEIRCE

NATE! IT'S ME, **DEREK!** FROM CHESS CAMP LAST SUMMER, REMEMBER?!

YEAH, SURE! HI, DEREK, WHAT'S UP?

WHAT'S **UP**? WE'RE FIRST ROUND **OPPONENTS**, THAT'S WHAT'S UP! CAN YOU **BELIEVE** WE'RE PLAYING EACH OTHER? WHAT A **COINCIDENCE!**

REMEMBER WHAT A GREAT TIME WE HAD AT CHESS CAMP? REMEMBER WHAT **PALS** WE WERE? REMEMBER HOW **INSEPARABLE** WE WERE??

FRIEND OF YOURS?

AS A BARNACLE IS TO A ROCK.

REMEMBER SINGING CHESS SONGS AROUND THE CAMPFIRE?

ISN'T THIS JUST LIKE CHESS CAMP, NATE? YOU AND ME, PLAYING CHESS... JUST LIKE LAST SUMMER!

THINGS HAVE **CHANGED** A BIT SINCE THEN, THOUGH! I'VE BEEN **PRACTICING!** I'M NO LONGER IN **AWE** OF YOU!

OH, YOU TAUGHT ME A FEW THINGS, AND I HAVEN'T FORGOTTEN THEM! IN FACT, YOU JUST MIGHT HAVE TAUGHT ME **TOO WELL!**

MAYBE, JUST **MAYBE**, THE STUDENT HAS SURPASSED THE...

CHECKMATE.

WELCOME PLAYERS! TRI-COUNTY SCHOLASTIC **CHESS** TOURNAMENT

REGISTER HERE →

HOW'RE YOU DOING SO FAR?

I WON MY FIRST MATCH!

PAT?

PAT BLEVINS OF AMESBURY MIDDLE SCHOOL VERSUS NATE WRIGHT OF P.S. 38!

HMM... THIS GUY DOESN'T LOOK TOO TOUGH!

STILL, HE'S IN THE WINNER'S BRACKET, SO MAYBE HE'S... HMM? HE'S **WHISTLING!**

WELL, EITHER HE'S NOT TAKING THE MATCH SERIOUSLY, OR... ?? WHA-?... NOW HE'S EATING **CHEEZ DOODLES!**

CRUNCH MUNCH

...AND WHAT SORT OF WEIRD MOVE IS **THAT**?... DOES THIS KID HAVE ANY IDEA WHAT HE'S **DOING?**

!! NOW I'VE SEEN **EVERYTHING!** HE'S READING A **COMIC BOOK!**

THIS KID'S **CLUELESS!** I'M GONNA BLOW HIM OFF THE BOARD!

HEL**LO**? IS HE GOING TO **DO** SOMETHING? DOES HE EVEN **KNOW** IT'S **HIS MOVE?**

CHECKMATE

HOW'RE YOU DOING SO FAR?

OH, SHUT UP.

NATE, WHY ON EARTH DID YOU DO YOUR DRAWING ASSIGNMENT IN A **BATH-ROOM STALL?**

I DIDN'T **SET OUT** TO DO IT THAT WAY!

I JUST HAPPENED TO BE DOODLING ONE DAY, AND IT TURNED INTO THE BEST DRAWING I'VE EVER DONE! SO I KEPT WORKING ON IT!

IT'S RIGHT IN HERE!

HEY!

DO YOU MIND?

MOVE IT ALONG, JEFF. WE'VE GOT AN ART CRITIQUE GOING ON HERE.

Peirce

PRINCIPAL NICHOLS! A CRIME HAS BEEN COMMITTED!

A CRIME?

SOMEONE **ERASED** THE DRAWING I DID IN THE BOYS' BATHROOM! I WENT IN THERE THIS MORNING AND MY MASTERPIECE WAS **GONE**!

IT'S AN **OUT-RAGE**!

HMM... OKAY... LET ME GET THIS STRAIGHT...

YOU **DREW** ON **SCHOOL PROPERTY**?

I CREATED "PUBLIC ART."

Peirce

...AND NOW FOR THE NEXT STEP... I MIX THEM IN WITH WATER!

NOW STEP BACK AND WATCH THE FIRE-WORKS, GANG! THEY SWIM! THEY SQUIRM! THEY DO FLIPS! THEY...

FOR FUTURE REFERENCE, "SEA MONKEYS" ARE NOT A VALID SUBJECT FOR A SCIENCE PROJECT.

I'LL WRITE THAT DOWN.

105

AAARGH! MY GRADE POINT AVERAGE IN SOCIAL STUDIES IS AN **84.2!**

SO? THAT'S **GOOD!**

BUT I NEED TO GET IT TO AN **85!** THEN MY DAD WILL LET ME START DOING EXTRA-CURRICULAR ACTIVITIES AGAIN!

MRS. GODFREY GIVES EXTRA CREDIT TO KIDS WHO VOLUNTEER TO BE HER "CLASS-ROOM HELPER."

OH, THE INDIGNITY.

YES?

WELL? DID YOU ASK MRS. GODFREY IF YOU COULD BE HER CLASSROOM HELPER?

I DID

SHE TURNED ME DOWN. SHE ALREADY HAS A HELPER.

TOO BAD, NATE. THAT WOULD'VE BEEN AN EASY WAY TO GET EXTRA CREDIT.

I'M KIND OF RELIEVED, ACTUALLY. BECOMING A HELPER FOR MRS. GODFREY MIGHT VERY WELL HAVE TURNED ME INTO.... INTO....

IT'S TOO AWFUL TO THINK ABOUT.

YES, MRS. GODFREY! COLLATED AND STAPLED! RIGHT AWAY, MRS. GODFREY!

SHLOX-TV presents...

SURVIVE... OR ELSE!!

with your host: **KEN DOOLITTLE**!!

Here we are again, friends, in the **Social Studies class-room** where our intrepid survivors have been **TRAPPED** since early September!

They've had to endure countless hardships...

Have we **EVER**! Lectures, film strips, pop quizzes... Oh, the **HORROR**!

whimper

...And it's all because of **MRS. GODFREY**! She's making it **IMPOSSIBLE** to survive in here!

NATE - 6th grade tribe

Hmm... Sounds like you want to vote Mrs. Godfrey **OUT** of the classroom!

Oh, I **DO**!

So do I!

Me too!

And me!

Well, Mrs. Godfrey, the survivors have voted, and it looks like you're —

HOLD it, Ken. I didn't cast **MY** vote.

But...

No buts! What these "survivors" think is **IRRELEVANT**! I'm not going **ANYWHERE**!

I run this classroom, and **I** decide who stays and who goes!

OKAY, WELL... I WAS SUPPOSED TO DO MY REPORT ON HENRY PATRICK, BUT BELIEVE ME, IT WASN'T EASY.

I MEAN, EITHER THIS GUY IS ONE OF THE MOST OBSCURE PEOPLE IN HISTORY, OR...

NATE, YOU WERE **SUPPOSED** TO DO A REPORT ON **PATRICK HENRY**!

HUH?... NO, THE SHEET YOU GAVE ME SAYS HENRY PATRICK!

HENRY, **COMMA**, PATRICK!

THAT'S ANOTHER THING: WHAT KIND OF FREAK HAS A **COMMA** FOR A MIDDLE NAME?

HOW COME **YOU** GOT AN A ON YOUR REPORT AND **I** ONLY GOT A **D+**?

BECAUSE **MINE** IS FIVE PAGES LONG, NEATLY WRITTEN, AND CAREFULLY RESEARCHED.

YOURS IS TWO PARAGRAPHS LONG, WITH A PICTURE OF A **NINJA** DRAWN IN THE MARGINS!

YEAH, BUT IT'S THE BEST NINJA I'VE EVER DONE!

WELL, WHEN YOU PUT IT **THAT** WAY... HELLO, HONOR ROLL!

I SHOULD GET **SOME** CREDIT FOR THE SWORD! CHECK OUT THIS SWORD!

I'M HERE TO PROTEST, MRS. GODFREY! YESTERDAY'S EXAM WAS **TOTALLY** UNFAIR!

IN WHAT WAY?

IN **EVERY** WAY! LIKE ALL OF YOUR "TESTS," IT WAS CULTURALLY BIASED!

IT **COMPLETELY** DISCRIMINATED AGAINST PEOPLE WHO COULDN'T CARE LESS ABOUT SOCIAL STUDIES!

YES, NATE. THAT WAS INTENTIONAL.

HENRY FORD! **GERALD** FORD! WHAT'S THE **DIFF?**

IT'S ASTONISHING THAT ANY BROTHER OF ELLEN WRIGHT'S WOULD HAND IN SUCH SLOPPY HOMEWORK.

COMPARING ME TO MY OLDER SISTER! MAN, DO I HATE THAT! IT'S SO **UNFAIR**!

I'M NOT HER, I'M **ME**! I'M MY OWN PERSON! I'VE GOT MY OWN SKILLS! MY OWN TALENTS! MY OWN UNIQUE ABILITIES!

SUCH AS YOUR UNCANNY IMPRESSION OF MRS. CZERWICKI EATING A "TATER TOT"?

... BUT DO I GET A **GRADE** FOR THAT? **NO!**

NATE WRIGHT, YEARBOOK PHOTOGRAPHER, AT YOUR SERVICE, MR. ROSA! I'LL BE LOOKING TO GET A GOOD CANDID PHOTO OF YOU LATER TODAY.

CANDIDS ARE SUPPOSED TO BE A **SURPRISE**, AREN'T THEY? IF YOU'RE GOING TO TAKE A CANDID PHOTO, WHY TELL ME BEFOREHAND?

I JUST THOUGHT YOU MIGHT APPRECIATE A LITTLE ADVANCE WARNING.

YOU KNOW... AFTER LAST YEAR'S UNFORTUNATE NOSE-PICKING INCIDENT.

I WAS GROOMING MY MUSTACHE.

EEEYAAWNN

CLICK!

WHAT I REALLY, REALLY NEED IS A CAMERA WITH A SILENCER.

MRS. GODFREY, WHY ARE YOU ALWAYS MAKING US MEMORIZE ALL THESE HISTORICAL DATES? WHY DO WE HAVE TO BE SO **EXACT** ABOUT IT?

I KNOW WHAT THE LOUISIANA PURCHASE WAS! I KNOW HOW IMPORTANT IT WAS! SO WHY DO I NEED TO MEMORIZE THE EXACT YEAR IT HAPPENED? WHY?...**WHY?**

IN CASE YOU END UP BEING TESTED ON IT.

DID YOU EVER STOP TO THINK ABOUT THE SIMILARITIES BETWEEN SCHOOL AND THE INSURANCE INDUSTRY?

Peirce

DO YOU THINK PEOPLE SEE ME IN A DIFFERENT LIGHT NOW?

WHATTA YA MEAN?

I MEAN, I'M MAINTAINING A "B" AVERAGE NOW! I'M GETTING GOOD GRADES! I'M PRACTICALLY ON THE HONOR ROLL!

BUT I DON'T WANT PEOPLE TO START THINKING OF ME AS SOME POINTY-HEADED, SUPER SMART INTELLECTUAL!

I THINK YOU'RE SAFE THERE.

THERE'S NO "Y" IN "EUROPE."

WELL, GODFREY WON'T YELL AT ME WHEN I HAND IN **THIS** HOMEWORK! NO WRINKLES, NO RIPS, NO FOOD STAINS... IT'S **PERFECT!**

I EVEN **PRINTED IT OUT** ON THE COMPUTER, ON A BRAND-NEW CRISP SHEET OF... **OW!** PAPER CUT!

DANG!... I'M... HEY, TEDDY, DO YOU HAVE A TISSUE?... HEY, SOMEBODY GET ME A "BAND-AID"! OW! OWOWOW!

ARE THESE **BLOOD STAINS**?

I'M JINXED.

NATE!

YIP!

WOULD YOU MIND EXPLAINING **WHY** YOU'RE BRINGING A **ROCK** INTO SCHOOL?!

IT'S A COUNTER-WEIGHT!

A COUNTER-WEIGHT.

SO I WON'T TIP OVER!

MY BACKPACK IS SO LOADED DOWN WITH HOMEWORK I CAN'T **WALK** NORMALLY!

IF I DON'T HOLD THIS ROCK OUT IN FRONT OF ME, I'LL TOPPLE OVER **BACK-WARD!**

NATE, THAT IS THE MOST **RIDICULOUS** THING I'VE EVER HEARD! DROP THAT ROCK! **NOW!!**

WONK!

WUMP!

I CAN SEE GET-TING DETENTION FOR THIS, BUT IF SHE STEPS ON ME, THAT'S WAY TOO HARSH.

OKAY, FIRST LET'S DECIDE WHAT THE THEME OF OUR DANCE SHOULD BE!

HOW'S **THIS** FOR A THEME:

THE 6TH GRADE GIRLS ACTUALLY **DANCE** WITH THE 6TH GRADE BOYS, INSTEAD OF THROWING THEMSELVES AT THE 7TH AND 8TH GRADE BOYS AND LEAVING THE 6TH GRADE BOYS STANDING AROUND EATING SOUR CREAM AND ONION CHIPS AT THE **SNACK TABLE!**

OKAY, MOVING RIGHT ALONG...

I DON'T THINK THAT'LL FIT ON A POSTER, MAN.

★☆★☆★☆★☆★ Time For Another Scintillating Edition OF...

FACULTY INTERVIEW!

with your host: **CHIP CHIPSON!**

Hello, friends! Today I'm chatting with P.S. 38's "Jabba the Hutt" look-alike... Social Studies teacher **MRS. GODFREY**!!

Can't talk now. I'm busy.

Ah! I see you're correcting **NATE WRIGHT's** most recent test!

That's right, Chip, and he is **FAILING** miserably!

And yet... you seem **HAPPY** about that!

Of **COURSE** I'm happy about it! That's what **I WANTED** to happen!

I... I don't understand.

I told Nate to study Chapter Three! **Then** I tested him on Chapter **TWELVE!**

But... that's totally **UNFAIR!**

Exactly! That's how he'll **LEARN:** by absorbing **DEFEAT** after devastating **DEFEAT!**

You've got to **BREAK** kids' **spirits** while they're young, Chip! Sure, it may seem cruel... but deep down they **LOVE** you for it!

OH, HOW I LOATHE HER.

JUST AN OBSERVATION: THERE WERE NO MATADORS AT THE BATTLE OF BULL RUN.

MR. GALVIN, HOW COME WE NEVER DO ANYTHING COOL IN SCIENCE?

"COOL"?

LIKE **CLONING**! CAN'T WE TRY TO **CLONE** SOMETHING? PLEASE? LET'S CLONE SOMETHING!

OR SOME**ONE**! **HEY**! **I'LL** VOLUNTEER! **I'D** GET CLONED IN A **HEART**BEAT! LET'S CLONE **ME**!

SPEAKING FOR THE FACULTY, NATE, ONE OF YOU IS QUITE ENOUGH.

I'LL SEND MY **CLONE** TO SOCIAL STUDIES, WHILE **I** WATCH CARTOONS IN THE A.V. ROOM!

...BUT WHY **CAN'T** I CLONE MYSELF?

NATE, WHAT YOU'RE TALKING ABOUT IS **SCIENCE FICTION!**

NOT ONLY IS CLONING OF HUMAN BEINGS STILL ONLY THEORETICAL, THERE ARE MANY **OTHER** ISSUES OF...

AH, AH! I KNOW WHAT YOU'RE GOING TO SAY, MR. GALVIN!

...AND I ASSURE YOU I HAVE NO PROBLEMS AT ALL WITH THE **ETHICAL RAMIFICATIONS** OF CLONING MYSELF!

WHY DOESN'T THAT SURPRISE ME?

NOW IF **MRS. GODFREY** WANTED TO GET CLONED!... **THEN** WE'D HAVE A PROBLEM!

Peirce

1.) Carl is taking a math test. There are 10 questions which take 30 seconds each; 15 questions which take 40 seconds each; and 12 questions which take two minutes each.

Carl pauses for 5 seconds between questions. In addition, he sharpens his pencil twice, which takes 20 seconds each time. The test begins promptly at 10:00 am. When Carl hands in his completed test,

what time is it?

143

UH... MRS. GODFREY? WHEN YOU HANDED BACK OUR REPORTS, MINE DIDN'T HAVE A GRADE ON IT.

YES, I KNOW.

IF YOU'RE NOT GOING TO PUT ANY EFFORT INTO WRITING YOUR REPORTS, I'M NOT GOING TO PUT ANY EFFORT INTO **GRADING** THEM.

SOMETHING JUST HAPPENED THAT'S EITHER VERY, VERY GOOD OR VERY, VERY BAD.

YOU'LL HAVE 45 MINUTES TO COMPLETE THIS TEST.

OKAY, HERE WE GO! NUMBER ONE!...

I'LL COME BACK TO THAT ONE.

NUMBER TWO...

UMM.... I'LL COME BACK TO THAT ONE, TOO.

NUMBER THREE... HEY, WHAT **IS** THIS? I HARDLY KNOW **ANY** OF THESE!

mumble

huh?

?

?

?

grumble

WHOOPS! MY APOLOGIES, PEOPLE! I GAVE YOU THE **WRONG TEST!**

I GAVE YOU THE TEST FOR MY **OTHER** CLASS! THEY'RE TWO CHAPTERS AHEAD OF YOU!

HERE'S THE **RIGHT** TEST!

AS I SAID, YOU HAVE 45 MINUTES.

OKAY! NUMBER ONE!

CAN I HAVE THE OTHER TEST BACK?

NATE! REMEMBER WHEN WE FOUND OUT THAT MR. ROSA IS GOOD AT BASKETBALL? IT GAVE ME AN IDEA!

A KIDS VS. TEACHERS BASKETBALL GAME! WOULDN'T THAT BE A **BLAST?**

NATE! I SAID, DON'T YOU THINK THAT WOULD BE A BLAST?

NATE? I WANT IT UNDERSTOOD I REFUSE TO PLAY "IN-YOUR-FACE" DEFENSE AGAINST MRS. GODFREY.

WHAT'S **THAT** SUPPOSED TO MEAN?

JUST WHAT IT SAYS!

ANYTHING FOR $1

FOR ONLY A DOLLAR, I CAN SEARCH MY VAST INVENTORY FOR ANY-THING THE BUYER WANTS!

ANYTHING? YUH, **RIGHT!**

HERE'S A BUCK! GIMME A DOZEN DONUTS! **JELLY-FILLED!**

A DOZEN JELLY-FILLED! COMIN' UP!

RUSTLE RUSTLE

VOILA!

WOW!

HEY, THAT'S **GOOD!** LET **ME** TRY!

CERTAINLY, MY GOOD MAN!

WHAT CAN I GET YOU FOR **YOUR** DOLLAR?

A 10-DOLLAR BILL.

A 10-DOLLAR BILL! COMIN' RIGHT...

ANY... CLOSED

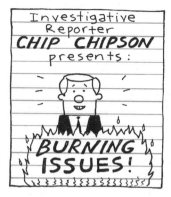

Investigative Reporter **CHIP CHIPSON** presents:

BURNING ISSUES!

Friends, today's "burning issue" is BULLYING! And here to discuss it is celebrity psychologist **DR. WARREN FUZZY!**

Chip, bullying is the scourge of our schools!

We all remember what it's like to be bullied! We've all felt **POWERLESS!**

...but what we **DON'T REALIZE** is how powerless the **BULLIES** feel!

The **BULLIES** feel powerless??

Right, Chip! That's why they're bullies!

They're **COMPENSATING** for their underlying sense of inadequacy! Underneath, they're **COWARDS!**

Once we know that, we can **STAND UP** to the bullies and **STOP** the cycle of bullying!

NATE.

HMM?

I'M WATCHING YOU, MISTER.

Does that really work?

Unless they're teachers. Then you just live in fear.

Peirce

161

LOOK! WE MUST BE HAVING A FILM-STRIP TODAY!

YESSSS! A FILM-STRIP!

NATE, WILL YOU RUN THE PROJECTOR?

ME? I GOTTA RUN THE PROJECTOR?

BUT THEN I WON'T BE ABLE TO SLEE—!

PARDON?

...TO SLA—... SLOO...SLI... SLIDE! TO SLIDE INTO MY SEAT AND GIVE THE FILMSTRIP MY FULL ATTENTION!

Peirce

MY REPORT TODAY IS ON THE REPUBLIC OF CAMERON, WHICH IS A PRETTY COOL NAME FOR A COUNTRY, IF YOU ASK ME.

I MEAN, I'VE GOT A **COUSIN** NAMED CAMERON. IT'S LIKE... "HI, I'VE GOT A WHOLE **COUNTRY** NAMED AFTER ME!" ISN'T THAT—

IT'S CAME**ROON**, NATE. YOU'RE LEAVING OUT A LETTER.

O.

NICE MOVE, NATE! DOING YOUR REPORT ON THE REPUBLIC OF **CAMERON** INSTEAD OF **CAMEROON!**

HA HA HEE HEE

SO? IT WAS A **MISTAKE**, THAT'S ALL! AREN'T I ENTITLED TO ONE MISTAKE?

ONE MISTAKE, YES! BUT YOU'VE DONE THIS **BEFORE!**

REMEMBER HIS REPORT ON THE "WHIG" PARTY?

WHEN HE BROUGHT IN THAT TOUPEE?

167

THAT'S A **SHAM**, FRANCIS! ARTUR'S ONLY PRE**TEND**-ING TO BE MY FRIEND! HE'S A **TWO·FACE**! HE'S A TOTAL **PHONY**!

TEN PAGES! I CAN'T BELIEVE GODFREY EXPECTS US TO WRITE **TEN PAGES!**

NATE. WHY ALWAYS DO YOU COMPLAIN ABOUT MRS. GODFREY?

WHY? BECAUSE THAT'S WHAT WE **DO**, ARTUR! WE'RE **STUDENTS!** STUDENTS COMPLAIN ABOUT TEACHERS!

YOU TRY IT, ARTUR! COMPLAIN ABOUT A TEACHER! **ANY** TEACHER!

CANNOT THINK OF ANY-THING BAD TO SAY.

I'M HAVING A HARD TIME FORMING A POSITIVE WORKING RELATIONSHIP WITH MY RESEARCH PARTNER.

ARTUR IS HOPELESS! I'M GOING TO TUTOR HIM.

TUTOR HIM? IN **WHAT**?

CRITICIZING PEOPLE! ARTUR HAS NO **CLUE** HOW TO RIP A TEACHER! HE'S UNSCHOOLED IN THE FINE ART OF THE PUTDOWN!

SO YOU'RE GOING TO TEACH ARTUR HOW TO SAY INSULTING THINGS ABOUT OTHER PEOPLE.

EXACTLY!

YOU'RE SUCH AN IDIOT.

RIGHT, STUFF LIKE THAT. ONLY MORE IMAGINATIVE.

SO?... DID YOU SUCCEED IN GETTING ARTUR TO CRITICIZE MRS. GODFREY?

NOPE.

I FINALLY REALIZED IT WASN'T AN **ACT**! ARTUR IS **LITERALLY** INCAPABLE OF SAYING AN UNKIND WORD ABOUT ANYONE!

HE'S A NICE KID. HE'S PROBABLY THE NICEST KID I'VE EVER MET.

OH, HOW I HATE HIM.

Peirce

MRS. SHIPULSKI, I'M WORKING ON THE NEXT ISSUE OF "CLASSROOM CHATTERS", AND...

HOLD IT RIGHT THERE, NATE!

I WILL **NOT** BE INTERVIEWED FOR YOUR **GOSSIP COLUMN!** YOU'VE MISQUOTED ME **TOO MANY TIMES!**

"SHIPULSKI MUM ON RUMORS."

RUMORS? WAIT A MINUTE! YOU DIDN'T SAY ANYTHING ABOUT...

"SHIPULSKI PLEADS IGNORANCE AS SCANDAL INTENSIFIES."

SCANDAL?? SCANDAL??

"SECRETARY SNAPS."

Peirce

183

FRANCIS! DID YOU KNOW THAT NATE CAN **SMELL** MRS. GODFREY FROM A MILE AWAY?

NOT JUST MRS. GODFREY! **ANY** TEACHER!

ALL TEACHERS HAVE THEIR OWN UNIQUE **SCENTS**, MY FRIENDS! AND THANKS TO MY AMAZING SENSE OF SMELL, I KNOW 'EM ALL!

MR. GALVIN, FOR EXAMPLE, IS A BEWITCHING BLEND OF CHALK, RUBBING ALCOHOL, TEABERRY GUM, FORMALDEHYDE, SHOE POLISH, "OLD SPICE" AND UNIDENTIFIED!

"UNIDENTIFIED"?

I DON'T LIKE THE SOUND OF THAT.

I'VE NARROWED IT DOWN. IT'S EITHER B.O. OR SOME KIND OF DEAD ANIMAL.

OK, HERE COMES ANOTHER TEACHER!

YEAH, NATE! "NAME THAT TEACHER!"

SNIFF SNIFF

HMM... I'M GETTING A DISTINCT WHIFF OF ROSE PETALS... ☆SNIFF!☆ ...SO IT'S GOT TO BE MS. LA CHANCE!

HELLO, BOYS.

MR. STAPLES MIGHT WANT TO CONSIDER USING SOAP THAT'S A BIT MORE MACHO.

※SNIFF!※ I'M GETTING A WHIFF OF ACRYLIC PAINT, CLAY AND RUBBER CEMENT! MR. ROSA MUST BE CLOSE BY!

CORRECT!

BUT... ※SNIFF!※... THERE'S SOMETHING **ELSE!**... I'M SMELLING **MRS. GODFREY'S** SCENT ON MR. ROSA! WHICH CAN ONLY MEAN THAT...

... MR. ROSA AND MRS. GODFREY ARE HAVING AN **AFFAIR!!**

OR, THERE COULD BE ANOTHER EXPLANATION...

PLEASE, TEDDY. I'M THE EXPERT HERE.

Peirce

HEY, LOOK WHAT I'VE GOT! THE BRAND-NEW EDITION OF THE "BOOK OF FACTS"!

OH, NO.

BEFORE YOU SAY ANYTHING MORE, FRANCIS, **PROMISE** ME YOU'RE NOT GOING TO BORE ME TO THE POINT OF INSANITY BY READING OUT LOUD FROM THAT **BOOK** ALL DAY!

SORRY. I CAN'T PROMISE THAT.

SAY, HERE'S A LITTLE-KNOWN FACT ABOUT SOLAR ECLIPSES! DID YOU KNOW THAT TOTAL SOLAR ECLIPSES ACTUALLY TAKE PLACE NEARLY AS OFTEN AS TOTAL LUNAR ECLIPSES! THEY OCCUR AT A RATE OF ABOUT EVERY...

SOME-BODY SHOOT ME.

"LITTLE-KNOWN FACTS" ARE **CALLED** "LITTLE-KNOWN FACTS" BECAUSE SO **LITTLE** IS **KNOWN** ABOUT THEM!

WON MY MATCH!

NICE JOB, NATE! YOU PLAYED WELL!

NOW IF ARTUR CAN WIN **HIS** MATCH, WE'LL WIN THE TOURNAMENT!

OH, GREAT.

SO, FOR A **CHANGE**, ARTUR WILL BE THE **HERO** AND EVERYONE WILL BE TALKING FOR **WEEKS** ABOUT HOW GREAT ARTUR IS!

AND WE'LL WIN THE TOURNAMENT.

THANKS TO "MR. WONDER-FUL"!

Peirce

I'M CONFLICTED. I DON'T KNOW WHETHER I WANT ARTUR TO WIN HIS MATCH OR NOT.

IF HE WINS, THEN WE WIN THE TOURNAMENT, AND THAT'S GOOD!...

BUT HE'LL ALSO GET ALL THE GLORY, WHICH IS **BAD!**

THEN AGAIN, I **DO** WANT US TO WIN!

...BUT I ALSO KIND OF WANT ARTUR TO **LOSE!**

BUT WHY CAN'T I JUST BE **HAPPY** FOR ARTUR'S SUCCESS?

BE**CAUSE!** HASN'T HE HAD **ENOUGH** SUC-CESS?

BUT THAT'S SO SHALLOW!

SHALLOW, SH**MALL**OW! LET HIM GO **DOWN!**

IT'S LIKE BEING TEAM-MATES WITH GOLLUM.

I CAN'T BELIEVE ARTUR **LOST**! THAT'S **AWFUL**!

OH, GIVE ME A BREAK, NATE! YOU'RE **THRILLED**! YOU THINK OF ARTUR AS A **RIVAL**, NOT A TEAMMATE!

WELL, YOU CAN STAY HERE AND GLOAT OVER HIS LOSS! **I'M** GONNA GO THANK HIM FOR DOING THE BEST HE COULD!

NATE? I'VE BEEN WATCHING. IT'S VERY KIND OF YOU TO TRY TO CONSOLE ARTUR.

TRI-
INVI
CH

IT'S PROBABLY NOT EASY FOR YOU. I REALIZE THAT YOU AND HE HAVE A BIT OF A RIVALRY.

...SO I JUST WANTED TO SAY THAT I APPRECIATE YOUR PUTTING YOUR PERSONAL FEELINGS ASIDE AND THINKING OF A TEAM-MATE FIRST!

HERE COMES THE SPELLING LESSON.

...BECAUSE THERE'S NO "I" IN **TEAM**!

Peirce

221